# Contents

Schofield & Si

# Section 1 Test 1

## A WARM-UP

**hall paint**

Use these words to write

1 **a complex sentence:** ____________________

____________________

____________________

2 **a question:** ____________________

____________________

____________________

Write two adverbs that give contrasting pictures.

3 She got up __________ / __________.

4 He smiled __________ / __________.

5 He spoke __________ / __________.

6 She stood __________ / __________.

Underline the hidden four-, five- or six-letter word.

7 S P T E S U R E P L D E

8 D A W F U L T H O S K

9 C L S C H O L W E I R D L E

10 C H E C T I C L E N P L E

## B WORD WORK

Complete the verb table.

| | | + ing | + ed |
|---|---|---|---|
| 1 | control | | |
| 2 | happen | | |

Complete the adjective table.

| | | + y | + er | + est |
|---|---|---|---|---|
| 3 | fun | | | |
| 4 | ice | | | |

Write the word showing its root word and affixes.

5 immortality ______ / ______ / ______

6 inexpensive ______ / ______ / ______

Underline the correct word.

7 The driver was (braking / breaking) hard.

8 Two eagles (saw / sore / soar) overhead.

9 There was a (freeze / frieze) on the wall.

10 The words in brackets are called __________

because ____________________

____________________

## C SENTENCE WORK

Add subordinate clauses to the beginning, middle and end of the sentence.

1 ____________________ Zack looked away quickly.

2 Zack ____________________ looked away quickly.

3 Zack looked away quickly ____________________

Add the commas, full stops and capital letters.

4 waiting for Sita Jenny saw a man leaving the house she had seen him before he had been in the car that night.

5 we make needless car journeys leave countless electrical appliances on standby and waste the world's natural resources. yet no-one seems to care

Add a prepositional phrase after the noun so that the directions are clear.

6 Look for a gate ____________________

7 Cross the stream ____________________

8 Head for the stile ____________________

9 Turn left through a gate ____________________

10 Follow the path ____________________



X There is only one correct answer. X There is more than one correct answer.

# Section 1 Test 2

## A WARM-UP

Make the sentence into a compound sentence.

1 Joe was lost ______________________

______________________

2 There was a crash ______________________

______________________

3 She spun round ______________________

______________________

Underline the word that is spelt correctly.

4 color sorce score contor

5 wership werse fern jernal

Write correctly the words that are wrongly spelt.

6 4: ______________________

7 5: ______________________

Complete the words to make a word that ends and a word that starts with the root.

8 ________graph graph________

9 ________dent dent________

10 ________port port________

## B WORD WORK

1 Underline the words that have a soft **c**.

decision critic process cursor

incisor score cancel mercy

2 A soft **c** is usually followed by the letters

______________________

3 Add **c** or **s**.

coun__il jui__y in__ect pro__ess

ten__e sy__tem re__ipe re__ult

4 Add the correct antonym prefix.

____familiar ____attentive

____probable ____-violent

Use a prefix to write the word that means

5 **not noticed:** ______________

6 **not regular:** ______________

7 **not legal:** ______________

8 **not mature:** ______________

Write a sentence that shows the meaning.

9 **minor:** ______________________

10 **miner:** ______________________

______________________

## C SENTENCE WORK

Write a complex sentence starting with the non-finite verb.

1 Hobbling ______________________

2 Stunned ______________________

3 Realising ______________________

4 Hounded ______________________

Explain why a dash has been used in each example.

5 The porridge was cold and lumpy – yuck! ______________________

6 Lucy clambered to her feet – she was not defeated yet. ______________________

7 "I thought I heard –" began Ricky. ______________________

Write a sentence to show how the tense might be used in a promotional leaflet describing a stately home.

8 **past:** ______________________

9 **present:** ______________________

10 **future:** ______________________

X There is only one correct answer. X There is more than one correct answer.

# Section 1 Test 3

## A WARM-UP

Continue each sentence using a different subordinating connective.

1 Ben smiled ______________________

2 Ben smiled ______________________

3 Ben smiled ______________________

______________________

Complete the well-known saying.

4 __________ give up the day job.

5 Crime __________ pay.

6 You __________ take it with you.

7 Add the same grapheme to all the words.

__tumn appl__se s__sage __dience

8 Which word sounds different?

__________

9 Add the same grapheme to all the words.

__sel m__gre l__gue w__lth

10 Which word sounds different?

__________

## B WORD WORK

Add the missing vowels.

1 gall_ry fact_ry libr_ry qu_y

2 pen_lty inj_ry troph_ voll_y

Write all the words as plurals.

3 1: ______________________

4 2: ______________________

5 Make six words using these word parts only.

**contra pre re dict view tion**

______________________

______________________

Write the meaning of the prefix.

6 **contra:** __________ 8 **re:** __________

7 **pre:** __________

Write a sentence that shows the meaning.

9 **bought:** ______________________

______________________

10 **brought:** ______________________

______________________

## C SENTENCE WORK

Complete the conditional sentence using one of these words. Use a different word in each sentence.

**if, as long as, provided that, unless**

1 There will be a drought ______________________

2 People will come to the car boot sale ______________________

3 There is no danger ______________________

4 Jackson would have won ______________________

Add the missing comma or commas. Give a reason for their use.

5 You will come to the party won't you? ______________________

6 Busy writing she hardly noticed Jo enter. ______________________

7 The third woman had red hair a thin face steely eyes and an unpleasant snarl.

______________________

8 In conclusion, this would seem to be the way forward. ______________________

9 Underline the verbs.

Jack whirled round, slipping in the mud, grasping a branch.

10 What effect is created by the verbs used?

______________________



X There is only one correct answer. X There is more than one correct answer.

# Section 1 Test 4

## A WARM-UP

Write three sentences describing different aspects of the same **door**.

1 **simple:** ____________________

2 **compound:** ____________________

____________________

____________________

3 **complex:** ____________________

____________________

____________________

Continue the compound word chain.

4 internet – **net**_______ – _______

5 high**light** – _______ – _______

6 further**more** – _______ – _______

Write as a word.

7 40 _______

8 8th _______

9 90 _______

10 12th _______

## B WORD WORK

Write the words correctly.

1 easly _______ desprate _______

2 Cathlic _______ journlist _______

3 What is wrong with all the misspelt words?

____________________

4 What technique might help you to remember the correct spellings?

____________________

____________________

Underline the word that is spelt correctly.

5 definatly definitely definately

6 entrence enterance entrance

7 Add the same consonant suffix to each word.

command_____ advertise_____ settle_____

8 The suffix changes the verbs into _______ .

9 Add the same vowel suffix to each word.

acid___ photograph___ athlete___

10 The suffix changes the nouns into _______ .

## C SENTENCE WORK

1 Rewrite the sentence in the passive form.

The third marquis built the house. ____________________

2 How is the passive version different? ____________________

____________________

Rewrite the headline in the passive form.

3 Snake bites man ____________________

4 Council closes Skate Park ____________________

Sam is scared of Marcie. Show this

5 **using a line of dialogue:** ____________________

6 **by describing the behaviour of the character/s:** ____________________

Add a colon and complete the sentence.

7 There are three main types of sentence ____________________

8 This is how my favourite poem begins ____________________

9 There is only one option ____________________

10 Final score ____________________

X There is only one correct answer. X There is more than one correct answer.

# Section 1 Test 5

## A WARM-UP

Write a sentence to show how the tense might be used in an autobiography.

1 **past:** ____________________

2 **present:** ____________________

3 **future:** ____________________

Underline the antonym.

4 **regular** irregular unregular iregular

5 **literate** inliterate illiterate unliterate

6 **appear** dissappear disappear reappear

7 **named** unamed illnamed unnamed

8 **inform** disinform uninform misinform

9 Add a short word to complete the longer word.

comfor____ env____ment a____rophe

10 Add the same short word to complete all three longer words.

lis____ing po____tial in____sive

## B WORD WORK

Add the suffix **ly**.

1 love____ sure____ actual____

2 whole____ responsible____ able____

3 Write the meaning of the prefix.

**auto:** ____________

**prim(us):** ____________

**trans:** ____________

Write three words derived from the prefix.

4 **auto** ____________________

5 **prim** ____________________

6 **trans** ____________________

Write the modern word that means the same.

7 **nay:** ____________

8 **thou:** ____________

9 **thee:** ____________

10 **hast:** ____________

## C SENTENCE WORK

Rewrite the sentence so that the information given in brackets is embedded within it.

1 Rosalind was completely fearless. (She was elderly.)

____________________

2 His trainers were now ruined. (They were brand new.)

____________________

3 Mr Khan shuffled from behind the counter. (He was grumbling under his breath.)

____________________

Put a tick if the comma is used correctly. Put a cross if it is not.

4 It was getting dark, the bus was late. ____

5 The animals fled, scenting fear and death. ____

6 France is an interesting country, the scenery is beautiful. ____

7 This book is great, you should read it. ____

8 Explain why some commas were used incorrectly. ____________________

____________________

Write a definition.

9 **biased:** ____________________

10 **balanced:** ____________________



X There is only one correct answer. X There is more than one correct answer.

# Section 1 Test 6

## A WARM-UP

Write a slogan for a new place to eat called Dan's Diner. Use

1 **alliteration:** ______________________________

______________________________

2 **rhyme:** ______________________________

______________________________

3 **word play:** ______________________________

Complete the rhyming homophone pairs.

4 **bear** and b_____ / m_____ and m_____

5 **right** and _____ / s_____ and s_____

6 **meat** and _____ / b_____ and b_____

7 **wait** and _____ / gr_____ and gr_____

8 Write the homophone.

**story** __________ **beach** __________

9 Write the plurals of all four words.

______________________________

10 Underline the word that is the same in singular and plural form.

mouse fungus sheep tooth

## B WORD WORK

1 Complete the grid.

| | + ed | + ing | + er |
|---|---|---|---|
| **supply** | | | |
| **travel** | | | |
| **ski** | | | |

Add the missing syllables.

2 in / _____ / _____ / _____ ***Clue:*** *listed in a recipe*

3 in / _____ / _____ / _____ ***Clue:*** *a lack of thanks*

4 in / _____ / _____ / _____ ***Clue:*** *able to influence*

5 in / _____ / _____ / _____ ***Clue:*** *unplanned break*

Add **er** or **or**.

6 curs___ comput___ monit___ sens___

7 direct___ narrat___ writ___ act___

Explain the derivation.

8 **sumo** ______________________________

9 **spotlight** ______________________________

______________________________

10 **motel** ______________________________

## C SENTENCE WORK

Complete the sentence.

1 If everyone used low-energy light bulbs ______________________________

2 Unless we act now to slow global warming ______________________________

3 If we continue to use water at the present rate ______________________________

4 What is the purpose of sentences like these? ______________________________

Rewrite the sentence, replacing the conjunction with a semi-colon.

5 I never eat peanuts because I have a nut allergy. ______________________________

6 The dog returned for a third time so he was clearly a determined creature.

______________________________

7 I shall not be going on the trip as we are short of money.

______________________________

Complete the sentences using verbs suggesting that the characters are both nervous and

8 **uncertain:** Jafar ______________________________

9 **frightened:** Mick ______________________________

10 **excited:** Backstage, the actors ______________________________

X There is only one correct answer. X There is more than one correct answer.

# Section 1 Test 7

## A WARM-UP

**leaves clown**

Use the words in

1 **a simple sentence:** ____________________

2 **a compound sentence:** ____________________

3 **a complex sentence:** ____________________

Add the letters needed for the missing vowel sound.

4 ***Clue:*** *music*

ch___d h___m___ny m___l___dy

5 ***Clue:*** *RE*

s___mb___l w___sh___p s___cr___d

6 ***Clue:*** *ICT*

h___dw___e spr___dsh___t m___m___y

Solve the anagram.

7 **hears:** __________ 9 **gates:** __________

8 **skid:** __________ 10 **tough:** __________

## B WORD WORK

1 Add **ie** or **ei**.

bel___ve f___rce rec___ve c___ling

2 What spelling rule did you use?

____________________

3 Add **ie** or **ei**.

n___ghbour for___gn consc___nce

4 The spelling rule does **not** apply to these words.

Why? ____________________

Add suffixes to make three more words.

5 **pity** ____________________

6 **fit** ____________________

7 **hope** ____________________

Sort the words according to the subject.
Some words may be used twice.

**virus digest modem display**
**portrait sketch pastel oxygen**

8 **ICT:** ____________________

9 **science:** ____________________

10 **art:** ____________________

## C SENTENCE WORK

Write a sentence to show how the sentence type might be used in a promotional leaflet describing a castle.

1 **statement:** ____________________

2 **exclamation:** ____________________

3 **directive:** ____________________

4 **question:** ____________________

5 Underline the adjectives.

Aunt Maud was wearing her usual beige cardigan, traditional plaid skirt and sensible flat shoes.

6 What impression do they create of Aunt Maud? ____________________

Write a sentence that makes Aunt Maud sound

7 **eccentric:** ____________________

8 **imposing:** ____________________

Add a dash and continue each sentence in a dramatic and interesting way.

9 Then he heard the driver's voice ____________________

10 The tomb was full of incredible treasures ____________________



**X** There is only one correct answer. **X** There is more than one correct answer.

# Section 1 Test 8

## A WARM-UP

Write a sentence to show how the tense might be used in a discussion about the importance of exercise.

1 **past:** ______________________________

______________________________

2 **present:** ______________________________

______________________________

3 **future:** ______________________________

______________________________

Complete the well-known saying using the name of an animal.

4 the ______ whiskers
6 the ______ knees
5 a ______ dinner
7 the ______ share

Use the mnemonic to write three words.

8 **G**et **r**eady **a**nd **p**lay **h**ard.

______________________________

9 **O**h **U** **n**aughty **t**iger!

______________________________

10 **A**lways **u**se **g**ood **h**umour.

______________________________

## B WORD WORK

Underline the unstressed vowel. Then split the word to show the root word and affix.

1 poisonous ________ / ________
2 reference ________ / ________
3 offering ________ / ________
4 Split each of the words into syllables.

____ / ____ / ____ ____ / ____ / ____

____ / ____ / ____

5 How do these techniques help to spell the words?

______________________________

Write two words with the prefix

6 **bi** (meaning **two**): ______________________________
7 **de** (meaning **undo**): ______________________________

Add the correct word.

**lighting lightening lightning**

8 A fork of ________ lit up the sky.
9 The sky was ________ as the cloud lifted.
10 The ________ for the scene was perfect.

## C SENTENCE WORK

Reorder the words to make three different sentences. **Kelly ran down the street searching frantically.**

1 ______________________________
2 ______________________________
3 ______________________________
4 Which version or versions focus most effectively on Kelly's feelings?

______________________________

Put a tick if the colon is used correctly. Put a cross if it is not.

5 On the desk there was: a pencil, a notebook and a telephone directory. ____
6 My favourite saying is: 'Look before you leap'. ____
7 There is only one team for me: Leeds United. ____

Add words or phrases before and after the nouns to modify them.

8 They reached the ______________ gates ______________
9 They found a ______________ garden ______________
10 There was the ______________ cave ______________

X There is only one correct answer. X There is more than one correct answer.

# Section 1 Test 9

## A WARM-UP

Use the words to make four sentences.

**Joe outside remorse filled waited with quietly**

1 ______________________________

______________________________

2 ______________________________

______________________________

3 ______________________________

______________________________

4 ______________________________

______________________________

Complete the sentence, using the short word that you add to complete the longer word.

5 You can ______ a char______er.

6 You can ______ a re______sal.

7 You can ______ stringed in______ents.

Write a word that ends and a word that starts with the grapheme.

8 ______ en en ______

9 ______ ic ic ______

10 ______ phy phy ______

## B WORD WORK

Add the suffix **able**.

1 respect______ stop______ suit______

2 envy______ rely______ pay______

3 adore______ dispose______ manage______

4 What class of words have you made? ______

5 What do you notice about the spelling of the words ending in **e**?

______________________________

______________________________

6 Add the same letter string to each word.

res____ce fl____ col____ j____ney

7 Why is this a tricky letter string? ______

______________________________

Write different definitions.

8 **score** (in PE): ______________________________

9 **score** (in design and technology): ______________________________

______________________________

10 **score** (in music): ______________________________

______________________________

## C SENTENCE WORK

Rewrite as three separate sentences.

**Now that the wind had dropped, the house was silent and nothing stirred.**

1 ______________________________

2 The effect of the short sentences is ______________________________

**They pounded on the door and they cried out but still there was no reply.**

3 ______________________________

4 The effect of the short sentences is ______________________________

5 Give two reasons for starting a new paragraph when you are writing a story.

______________________________

6 Here are some ways of ending a story. Write a brief note to explain each term.

**a cliffhanger:** ______________________________

**a final twist:** ______________________________

**a resolution:** ______________________________

Add a comma or a semi-colon.

7 Her eyes were red she'd been crying.

8 Something lurked waiting for me.

9 It was raining his bare feet were cold.

10 Shivering violently he reached out.



X There is only one correct answer. X There is more than one correct answer.

# Section 1 Test 10

## A WARM-UP

**It could snow tomorrow.**

Rewrite the sentence as

1 **a headline:** ______________________

______________________

2 **a rhyming couplet:**

______________________

______________________

3 **a complex sentence:** ______________________

______________________

______________________

Complete each word by adding

4 **an onomatopoeia:**

un____ular t____b ____bour

5 **a pronoun:**

jealo____ ____th ____ight

6 **a possessive pronoun:**

hum____ sp____e ____th

Write the homophone.

7 **profit** ______ 9 **rain** ______

8 **bite** ______ 10 **not** ______

## B WORD WORK

Add the correct 'shun' ending.

1 conjunc____ dimen____ nutri____

2 Rus____ A____ dieti____

3 conserva____ opposi____ prepara____

Add the same phoneme to all three words.

4 ____ysical gra____ic apostro____e

5 stoma____ ____emist a____e

6 s____stem d____nasty rh____thm

Write a definition of the word in **bold**.

7 a **brief** visit

brief: ______________________

8 a design **brief**

brief: ______________________

______________________

9 a **current** news story

current: ______________________

10 an electric **current**

current: ______________________

## C SENTENCE WORK

Complete the conditional sentence.

1 If the weather had been better, ______________________

2 If the river had continued to rise ______________________

3 If Mr Higgins had not seen us, ______________________

4 What is the purpose of sentences like these?

______________________

Add brackets.

5 In the south, summers December to March are cool and winters June to September are mild.

6 Some snakes inject venom poison into their prey through specially grooved fangs teeth.

7 Using brackets like this is called ______________. The brackets are used to ______________

______________________

Write a sentence using nouns and noun phrases to create an effect that is

8 **frightening:** ______________________

9 **welcoming:** ______________________

10 **unusual:** ______________________

______________________

X There is only one correct answer. X There is more than one correct answer.

# Section 1 Test 11

## A WARM-UP

Improve on the cliché.

1 as smooth as silk ______________________

______________________

2 as cold as ice ______________________

______________________

3 as warm as toast ______________________

______________________

Write the homophone pair.

4 **a female sheep:** __________

**a type of tree:** __________

5 **hairless:** __________

**wailed:** __________

6 **a male child:** __________

**a float or marker:** __________

Write a word that ends and a word that starts with each letter string.

7 ________gn gn________

8 ________gue gue________

9 ________mn mn________

10 ________cy cy________

## B WORD WORK

1 Add the missing letter.

autum_ clim_ colum_

2 Write the words correctly.

strenth __________ casle __________

rombus __________ musle __________

3 The same letter is silent in all the words. Underline it.

scenery scissors crescent resuscitate

4 Explain why it is silent. ______________________

______________________

Write two words with the same root.

5 **circulate** ______________________

6 **audible** ______________________

Write the meaning of the root.

7 **circu(m):** __________ 8 **audi:** __________

Write a definition of the word in **bold**.

9 Their first attempt was **sabotaged**.

sabotaged: ______________________

10 The girl had a **beguiling** manner.

beguiling: ______________________

## C SENTENCE WORK

Rewrite the sentence in the passive form, hiding those who perform the actions.

1 The council will reverse the decision. ______________________

2 Shop assistants turned many customers away. ______________________

3 The keepers feed the animals twice a day. ______________________

Add a question tag to turn the statement into a question.

4 This one is yours ______________________

5 We all want this ______________________

6 You will come ______________________

7 You can see my problem ______________________

8 Underline the verbs.

Reporters buzzed around the office, papers flying from hand to hand and keyboards clattering.

9 What impression does this create? ______________________

10 Describe a place with a sleepy atmosphere.

______________________



X There is only one correct answer. X There is more than one correct answer.

# Section 1 Test 12

## A WARM-UP

Write a sentence using these words.

**lion net**

1 **active sentence:** ______________________

______________________

2 **passive sentence:** ______________________

______________________

3 **question:** ______________________

______________________

4 **imperative:** ______________________

______________________

Complete the rhyming homophone pairs.

5 **air** and ________; w______ and ______

6 **ate** and ________; f______ and ______

7 **no** and ________; s______ and ______

8 **threw** and ________; b______ and ______

Solve the anagrams.

9 **Susie:** __________ **Leah:** __________

10 **Bertha:** __________ **Edgar:** __________

## B WORD WORK

Add the same ending to both words. **ary ery ory**

1 mem______ categ______

2 imagin______ sanctu______

3 flatt______ gall______

4 Circle the unstressed vowel in each ending.

5 What technique would help you to remember the correct ending? ______________________

______________________

6 Underline the words that have a soft **g**.

engage mega digit energy agog

7 A soft **g** is usually followed by the letters

__________

If these were real words, what would they mean? Write a definition.

8 **aquaport** (verb): ______________________

9 **automemory** (noun): ______________________

______________________

10 **superwealthy** (adjective): ______________________

## C SENTENCE WORK

Combine the three sentences into one.

1 He was tired. He walked on. Then he came to the river.

______________________

2 They drove past the field. Jenny waved at Billy. He was still digging.

______________________

3 I was walking home. I found a bag. It contained money.

______________________

4 Why do the original versions sound wrong?

______________________

Continue the line of dialogue.

5 She sighed and then asked ______________________

6 Peering from the window, Carrie said ______________________

7 A voice shouted ______________________

8 Underline the abstract nouns. Su stared at him with bewilderment and terror.

9 What is the purpose of the abstract nouns? ______________________

10 Write different abstract nouns for a different effect. Su stared at him with __________ and __________.

**Now complete Section 1 of the Progress chart on page 46.**

# Section 1 Writing task: After hours club

## Task

Your school is exploring the idea of setting up an 'after hours' club. Pupils will be able to use school facilities and take part in a range of activities after school. Your task is to write a letter to your headteacher or board of governors explaining your ideas for the club and persuading them that it is a good idea.

## Hints

Before you start:

- Think about the points you will make in the letter. What activities might you suggest? How will the club be organised and run?
- Decide how best to explain your ideas effectively and convincingly.
- Try to predict any concerns that the governors might have. Decide how you will deal with these and how you will make your ideas appealing.

As you write:

- Think about your purpose and audience.
- Choose your words carefully.
- Express yourself clearly and be sure to make your case persuasive.

*Continue on a separate sheet.*

## Check

- When you have finished, check through your writing.
- Edit and proofread it.
- Make sure that everything looks and sounds right.

# Section 1 Proofreading task: My favourite place

## Task

Proofread this description of a setting.

### Hints

- Check that everything is clear.
- Check the punctuation.
- Check the spelling.
- Change anything that does not look or sound right.

I realy do’nt rememmber much about my first jerney to the casel ownly the burning colers of the awtumn trees as we drived up the windding road and the delightfull sent of damp woodland.

I xpect Mrs Higgins was waiting to recieve us at the enterence enquireing about our jerney and provideing us with welcomeing drinks of hot choclate she usuly did allthogh I cant actuly rememmber that particuler time.

What I definitly do recall quiet clearley was wakeing the next morning to the bearly audable murmmur of the wind in the trees thats a memery I shall allways treshure.

The senary around the casel was quiet breathtakeing for a child like me used to sity life, living in a casel was such a huje advenchure, I loved the forist it was my privite advenchure playground.

I thought then and I still think now their is no more piecefull place or more beautifull rejion anywhere in the werld.

### Extra

On a separate sheet of paper, write a brief description of your own favourite place.

# Section 2 Test 1

## A WARM-UP

Modify the noun so that it describes a particular object in detail.

1 **door:** ______________________

______________________

2 **mirror:** ______________________

______________________

3 **lamp:** ______________________

______________________

4 **sandwich:** ______________________

______________________

Write another word that follows the same spelling pattern.

5 **length** __________

6 **count** __________

7 **sought** __________

Solve the anagram with a one-word answer.

8 **Love S:** __________

9 **Love N:** __________

10 **Love W:** __________

## B WORD WORK

Add the missing letters.

1 **cy sy**

___clone ___stem ___mbol ___nical

2 **ce se**

sour___ cour___ audien___ incen___

3 **ce se**

___real ___metery ___ptic ___rial

4 **g j**

a_ile sub_ect ad_acent di_est

5 Make six words using these roots and suffixes only.

**pure extreme ity ify ist ism**

______________________

______________________

6 Which suffix can make a verb? ______

Write a definition.

7 **resent** (verb): ______________________

8 **recent** (adjective): ______________________

9 **stationary** (adjective): ______________________

10 **stationery** (noun): ______________________

## C SENTENCE WORK

Underline the subordinate clause.

1 The book, which he found on the table, was now useless to him.

2 As the wind whispered gently, Lydia fell fast asleep.

3 They emerged from the cave, blinking in the sunlight.

4 Which subordinate clause begins with: **a conjunction?** _ **a relative pronoun?** _ **a non-finite verb?** _

5 You are writing a non-fiction text. What might be the most likely cue for starting a new paragraph in

**a recount of an event:** ______________ **a report on your local area:** ______________

**a discussion:** ______________

6 Give three ways in which the main point might be developed in the rest of the paragraph.

______________________________________________

Why has each colon been used?

7 Occupation: musician. ______________________

8 The story begins with these intriguing words: 'Once upon a cloud …' ______________

9 Debris was scattered down the road: bits of metal, a wheel, milk crates. ______________

10 His face was red: he had been running. ______________________

______________________________________________



X There is only one correct answer. X There is more than one correct answer.

# Section 2 Test 2

## A WARM-UP

Write four different types of sentence.

1 **active sentence:** The elephant ______________

______________________________

2 **passive sentence:** The elephant ______________

______________________________

3 **complex sentence:** The elephant ______________

______________________________

4 **exclamation:** The elephant ______________

______________________________

Underline the word that is **not** an abstract noun.

5 jealousy courage honest mischief

6 grief anguish distress desolate

7 peace freedom humane equality

Complete the mnemonic.

8 The ______ of a sove______ .

9 Make ______ you mea______ it.

10 Always ______ an ex______ation.

## B WORD WORK

1 Add the missing vowel phonemes.

secr__t__ry all__y all___gy cat__g__ry

terr__t__ry estu__ry b___y comp__ny

Should the word have a hyphen in the middle? Put a tick or a cross.

2 reaction ___

3 flowchart ___

4 nonfiction ___

5 grandfather ___

6 Write two words to follow the hyphen.

non-__________

non-__________

Write a sentence to show the meaning.

7 **course:** ______________________________

______________________________

8 **coarse:** ______________________________

______________________________

9 **sauce:** ______________________________

______________________________

10 **source:** ______________________________

______________________________

## C SENTENCE WORK

Complete the sentences, using a different subordinating conjunction in each one.

1 ______________________________ Susie felt sorry for him.

2 Susie felt sorry for the boy ______________________________

3 Susie felt sorry for the boy ______________________________

Is the semi-colon used correctly? Put a tick or a cross.

4 Australia is a great place to live; hot weather and beautiful beaches. ___

5 The children returned home; they had been away all week. ___

6 We enjoyed the holiday; despite the weather. ___

7 I rarely eat fatty foods; occasionally I fancy a cake. ___

8 Look at the sentences with a cross. In what way has the semi-colon been used incorrectly?

______________________________

You are writing an advertisement. What language features would you use and why?

9 **sentence structures:** ______________________________

______________________________

10 **stylistic techniques:** ______________________________

______________________________

X There is only one correct answer. X There is more than one correct answer.

# Section 2 Test 3

## A WARM-UP

Write a question-and-answer joke based on the homonym.

1 **crane:**

______________________________

______________________________

2 **bank:**

______________________________

______________________________

Complete the well-known saying.

3 ________ a star.

4 ________ blot ________ copybook!

5 ________ not over till ________ over.

Complete the word sum.

6 **regret + able + ly** = ________

7 **menace + ing + ly** = ________

8 **admit + ed + ly** = ________

9 **ir + regular + ly** = ________

10 **im+ polite + ly** = ________

## B WORD WORK

1 Complete the grid.

| | + ed | + ing | + al |
|---|---|---|---|
| **recite** | | | |
| **bury** | | | |
| **refer** | | | |

2 Add the prefix. **ab ad**

____join ____normal

Write the meaning of the prefix.

3 **ad:** ________ 4 **ab:** ________

Write four more words that show the meaning.

5 **ab** ______________________________

6 **ad** ______________________________

Write a modern question that means the same.

7 Where art thou? ________________

8 What would'st thou? ________________

9 Who hath dared to wound thee?

______________________________

10 How are the verbs different in the older version?

______________________________

______________________________

## C SENTENCE WORK

Rewrite the complex sentence, starting with a non-finite verb.

1 As he gathered his strength, he lifted the rock. ________________

2 Because she was filled with despair, she sat alone. ________________

3 Although he was groaning with pain, he stood up. ________________

4 What is the function of these subordinate clauses?

______________________________

Change the sentence to avoid any confusion over the pronouns used.

5 Rik entered Joe's room. He turned to face him.

6 Ali phoned Lal. He had found his dog.

7 Hilda and Ethel did not speak. She took off her coat and made her do the same.

Add the missing dashes to the sentence.

8 He was tall twice as tall as Nikki and wore a long coat.

9 Jack was not sure was not at all sure what he had seen.

10 Why are the dashes used?

______________________________



**X** There is only one correct answer. **X** There is more than one correct answer.

# Section 2 Test 4

## A WARM-UP

Write a sentence starting with the adverb given.

1 Nimbly ______

2 Viciously ______

3 Obstinately ______

4 Frantically ______

Add the same prefix to all three words.

5 ___ready ___mighty ___together

6 ___float ___board ___broad

7 ___organise ___possess ___produce

8 ____striker ____smoking ____existent

9 Write six words starting with **rh**.

______

______

10 Add the same missing letter to all six words.

g_ard g_ess g_itar

g_est g_ide g_ilt

## B WORD WORK

Write the words correctly.

1 physicly ______ basicly ______

personly ______ actuly ______

2 laboratry ______ boundry ______

3 machinry ______ threatning ______

Write the antonym pair.

4 ***Clue:*** *put together and take to pieces*

as / ___ / ___ and ______

5 ***Clue:*** *needed and not needed*

ne / ___ / ___ / ___ and ______

6 ***Clue:*** *applicable and not applicable*

rel / ___ / ___ and ______

7 ***Clue:*** *lasting and temporary*

per / ___ / ___ and ______

Add the same vowel suffix to all three words.

8 tour___ special___ extreme___

9 active___ agile___ mobile___

10 What class of words have you made? ______

## C SENTENCE WORK

Add a subordinate clause that begins with a relative pronoun.

1 The woman ______ was working in her allotment.

2 The bus ______ rattled down the road.

3 Marik and Simon met at Cypress Drive ______

4 Stella ______ stood in the doorway.

5 Add the punctuation and capital letters.

They froze what was that was it a footstep had someone found them they hardly dared breathe.

6 What effect has been created – and how? ______

______

7 Underline the simile.

**Angela was sleeping like a kitten, curled up amongst the filthy sacks.**

8 Why has the writer chosen this simile? ______

Write a simile to make the character sound

9 **pleasant:** Her laugh was ______

10 **unpleasant:** Her laugh was ______

X There is only one correct answer. X There is more than one correct answer.

# Section 2 Test 5

## A WARM-UP

Take the noun **car** and modify it to make four different noun phrases.

1 ____________________
2 ____________________
3 ____________________
4 ____________________

5 Underline the unstressed vowel.

parliament alcohol diary

chocolate vegetable

6 Write the words correctly.

natral ________ peple ________

dimond ________ miniture ________

Add a three- or four-letter word to complete the longer word.

7 po______ion
8 ex______ion
9 ent______ce
10 m______um

## B WORD WORK

Add **able** or **ible**.

1 ed_____ reput_____
2 leg_____ prob_____

Add **able** or **ible** to the root word.

3 response_____ enjoy_____ identify_____

Add the correct 'shun' ending.

4 exclude_____ equate_____ optic_____

Write different definitions for the words in **bold**.

5 It was a **physical** game.

physical: ____________________

6 **Physical** geography.

physical: ____________________

7 There was **friction** between the men.

friction: ____________________

8 There is **friction** on this surface.

friction: ____________________

Add the same suffix to all three words, to make nouns that name types of people.

9 chem____ flor____ cycl____
10 vegetar____ librar____ Christ____

## C SENTENCE WORK

**Oscar had to leave. He was tortured by his memories.**

Rewrite the two sentences as one. Do so in four different ways.

1 ____________________
2 ____________________
3 ____________________
4 ____________________

Add the punctuation and capital letters.

5 Take it she said it's worthless now
6 My big regret sighed Mr James is losing the medal
7 I'll never she said with dignity leave Park Street
8 My work is complete said Merlin now I must leave

9 Cross out the words that are not Standard English. Write them correctly.

We was winning easy. It was a real good game. ____________

He saw them cards what you dropped but he didn't do nothing to help. ____________

10 Give two examples of places where it might be appropriate to use non-Standard English in writing.

____________________



X There is only one correct answer. X There is more than one correct answer.

# Section 2 Test 6

## A WARM-UP

Write one shorter and one longer version of this sentence.

**Close by, a tawny owl hooted.**

1 ______________________

2 ______________________

______________________

Add a three- or four-letter word to complete the longer word. The shorter word starts with

3 **d:** con____sation in____ry evi____ce

4 **p:** re____ition hap____ed pro____ion

5 **m:** di____sion per____ent to____oes

Write two synonyms.

6 **nonchalantly** ______________________

7 **furtively** ______________________

8 **haughtily** ______________________

9 **jovially** ______________________

10 **obstinately** ______________________

## B WORD WORK

Add **ei** or **ie**.

1 perc___ve n___ce p___rce dec___ve

2 s___ze w___r prot___n n___ther

3 The words in 2 are tricky because ______________________

______________________

4 Add the suffix **ous**.

nerve____ outrage____ vigour____

5 Add the suffix **ity**.

mobile____ able____ generous____

6 Add the suffix **al**.

industry____ face____ nature____

Write a definition.

7 The path **petered out**.

petered out: ______________________

8 The **mesmerising** beat began again.

mesmerising: ______________________

9 The portrait is **enigmatic**.

enigmatic: ______________________

10 The event **culminated in** a disco.

culminated in: ______________________

## C SENTENCE WORK

Why has the writer used the passive form?

1 A man was killed in the incident. ______________________

2 The diamond was stolen. ______________________

3 The parcel was delivered. ______________________

4 The King was warmly applauded. ______________________

Add the apostrophes.

5 Brunels ship is one of Bristols main attractions.

6 Youll find the childrens playground behind Fishermans Cottage.

7 Both clubs managers are waiting to hear the FAs decision.

Rewrite the sentence to avoid ambiguity.

8 I saw a motorbike with a young man riding it with gleaming chrome.

______________________

9 The class visited a bakery to see bread being made on Wednesday.

______________________

10 That's the man with the dog who used to have a moustache.

______________________

X There is only one correct answer. X There is more than one correct answer.

# Section 2 Test 7

## A WARM-UP

Continue the sentence in different ways.

1 Joe wanted to believe her ____________________

2 Joe wanted to believe her ____________________

3 Joe wanted to believe her ____________________

4 Joe wanted to believe her ____________________

Add the missing letters.

**i y**

5 paral_se real_se c_cl_st d_et

6 c_nders t_p_cal d_sk ph_s_cal

Add the missing syllables.

7 per /______ /______ *Clue: a show*

8 ap /______ /______ *Clue: how things look*

9 ev /______ /______ *Clue: proof*

10 cir /______ /______ /______ *Clue: perimeter*

## B WORD WORK

Write three words ending with

1 **eight:** ____________________

2 **aught:** ____________________

Make three words by adding prefixes to the root word.

3 **active** ____________________

4 **face** ____________________

5 **scribe** ____________________

6 **claim** ____________________

Write sentences to show the different meanings of each word.

7 **freeze** (in science): ____________________

8 **freeze** (in drama): ____________________

9 **fibre** (in food): ____________________

10 **fibre** (in D&T): ____________________

## C SENTENCE WORK

Add a relative clause.

1 His coat ____________________ was gone.

2 Jenny ____________________ snapped at her brother.

3 In the forest ____________________ all was not well.

4 What is the purpose of a relative clause? ____________________

Add a colon and a second clause that expands on the first.

5 It was his first victory ____________________

6 She spoke calmly ____________________

7 Olivia was silent ____________________

8 The ground was dusty and cracked ____________________

**Mrs Modi and her neighbour were talking. She was almost deaf so she had to speak up. She was telling her about her cat.**

9 Why is this confusing? ____________________

10 Rewrite the text above so that the meaning is clear. ____________________



X There is only one correct answer. X There is more than one correct answer.

# Section 2 Test 8

## A WARM-UP

Create an acrostic phrase or sentence for the word

1 **snow:** ____________________

2 **dawn:** ____________________

3 **stream:** ____________________

____________________

4 Add the prefix.

**a ab ad**

___drift ___light ___olish ___opt

Add the correct antonym prefix.

5 ***Clue:** in maths*

___symmetrical ___regular ___equal

6 ***Clue:** in PE*

___active ___-striker ___mobile

7 ***Clue:** in science*

___vertebrate ___reversible ___soluble

Add the same three- or four-letter word to complete all three longer words.

8 con___rate in___ive inno___

9 am___ur m___rial cre___

10 awk___d re___d s___m

## B WORD WORK

Underline the word that is wrongly spelt.

1 chiefs shelfs beliefs reefs

2 scarves leaves rooves halves

3 tomatoes heroes volcanoes patioes

4 radios echos cellos ratios

One consonant or two? Add the missing letters.

5 a___o___odation di___a___oint

6 emba___a___ment reco___end

Underline the prefix and write the root word.

7 telecommunications ____________________

8 embolden ____________________

Write a definition.

9 **telecommunications:** ____________________

____________________

10 **embolden:** ____________________

## C SENTENCE WORK

Use commas to separate the different parts of the sentence.

1 After the clock struck that was when he first heard it the unmistakable sound of fear.

2 At the end of the corridor half-hidden in the murky light a hunched figure began to move.

3 There advancing towards him at a pace and with growing excitement was Sir Galahad.

4 How does the way the sentences are written build up tension? ____________________

____________________

**The fog wrapped itself darkly around the choking streets.**

5 What technique has the writer used? ____________________

6 What is its effect? ____________________

Complete the sentence and create a similar effect.

7 The ice ____________________

8 The sun ____________________

Express these ideas in a formal and impersonal style.

9 I hope you learn from this mistake. ____________________

____________________

10 Let's discuss this big issue. ____________________

**X There is only one correct answer.** **X There is more than one correct answer.**

# Section 2 Test 9

## A WARM-UP

Add a relative clause containing additional information.

1 Emily ______________________ wants to be a singer.

2 The ruby ______________________ glinted in the sunlight.

3 The street ______________________ was now deserted.

Write the word that has **both** meanings.

4 ________ : to worry/a part of a guitar

5 ________ : to set aside/a substitute

6 ________ : to dismiss from employment/a blaze

Continue the compound word chain.

7 touch**down** – **down**fall – ____________

8 may**fly** – ____________ – ____________

9 over**lap** – ____________ – ____________ – ____________

10 ear**ring** – ____________ – ____________ – ____________

## B WORD WORK

1 Add the letter(s) that make the 'sh' phoneme.

i____ue ma____ine ra____io an____ient

Add a 'shun' suffix and write the new word.

2 **repeat** ____________ 3 **reveal** ____________

4 This suffix turns the verbs into ____________

5 Add the same two letters to all the words.

frant____ tact____ electron____

6 Add one or more extra suffixes to each word.

______________________

7 Add a suffix that makes the words into verbs.

critic____ public____ character____

8 Write each word with a different suffix.

critic______ public______ character______

Write a definition.

9 **eco-tourist:** ______________________

10 **cyber-criminal:** ______________________

## C SENTENCE WORK

Move the subordinate clause to the start of the sentence.

1 The old woman shouted at the driver because she was angry.

______________________

2 The boy followed her, dragging the bag. ______________________

3 Sophie, who was hidden from view, felt safe. ______________________

4 In which sentence did you have to change the wording slightly and why?

______________________

Read this car advert. **Advanced design + innovative technology = optimum aerodynamic performance**

5 Describe the target audience. ______________________

Explain two stylistic techniques used to appeal to this target audience.

6 ______________________

7 ______________________

Use a semi-colon to continue the sentence.

8 There was an ornate box in the corner of the room ______________________

9 She looked again ______________________

10 The boy would not jump ______________________



X There is only one correct answer. X There is more than one correct answer.

# Section 2 Test 10

## A WARM-UP

Expand the nouns to provide information about the character.

1 **farmer:** ______________________________

______________________________

2 **lady:** ______________________________

______________________________

3 **puppy:** ______________________________

______________________________

4 **detective:** ______________________________

______________________________

Add the same suffix to make all three words into adjectives.

5 athlete_____ gymnast_____ energy_____

6 express_____ decorate_____ figure_____

7 danger_____ nerve_____ hazard_____

Add a three- or four-letter word to complete the longer word.

8 de_____ite

9 des_____ing

10 s_____ier

## B WORD WORK

1 Write the correct spelling.

vegetariun _________ religun _________

knowlidge _________ texchure _________

2 Write one other word with the same ending as each of the four words above.

______________________________

Change the suffix to make another word.

3 identity___

4 comprehension___

5 alliteration___

6 investigation___

7 Write three words derived from the word **compete**.

______________________________

Write a definition of the word in **bold**.

8 His face was **contorted** with pain.

contorted: ______________________________

9 As the tide went out the water **receded**.

recede: ______________________________

10 It is time to **implement** the plan.

implement: ______________________________

## C SENTENCE WORK

Make the sentences impersonal by rewriting them in the passive form.

1 We recorded the information on the database. ______________________________

2 We will provide all meals. ______________________________

3 You must return your application form by Friday. ______________________________

4 We gently heated the solution. ______________________________

5 Punctuate the sentence.

I'm telling you he was right there said Jenny pointing to the empty armchair.

6 What is the purpose of the last part of the sentence? ______________________________

Continue the sentence, combining dialogue and action.

7 "Take it ______________________________

8 "Excuse me ______________________________

**Allowing pupils to wear their own clothes to school could create a competitive environment.**

9 Underline the modal verb.

10 Why has the writer used it? ______________________________

______________________________

X There is only one correct answer. X There is more than one correct answer.

# Section 2 Test 11

## A WARM-UP

Open this sentence in three different ways.

1 ______________________
Josh glanced up.

2 ______________________
Josh glanced up.

3 ______________________
Josh glanced up.

Continue the compound word chain.

4 hence**forth** – **forth**with
– ________ – ________

5 whenever – ________
– ________ – ________

6 therefore – ________ – ________
– ________ – ________

7 forehead – ________ – ________
– ________ – ________

Underline the hidden four-letter word.

8 I C H F X L E D I E T A R

9 A E N A X I S M U Z T R S

10 E N T I O S O R O L E M

## B WORD WORK

Add the missing syllables to complete the noun.

1 con /____ /____ / tion ***Clue:*** *total focus*

2 pre /____ /____ /____ ***Clue:*** *groundwork*

3 con /____ /____ /____ ***Clue:*** *from gas to liquid*

4 com /____ /____ /____ ***Clue:*** *mixture*

5 Is the hyphen used correctly? Put a tick or a cross.

mock-up ___ re-act ___

non-smoking ___ a-lot ___

6 Write the incorrect words correctly.

______________________

Write a definition.

7 **podcast:** ______________________

8 **blogger:** ______________________

9 **cybercafé:** ______________________

10 **wiki:** ______________________

## C SENTENCE WORK

Rewrite the sentence so that the main focus comes at the end.

1 A sad cry came echoing over the hills. ______________________

2 The ghost was there, beside the door. ______________________

3 The Prince was sat calmly reading. ______________________

**Clouds paused; the river chuckled; the wind played with the reeds.**

4 Describe the mood of this sentence. ______________________

5 How is this effect created? ______________________

Write similar sentences to create a mood that is

6 **sinister:** ______________________

7 **frantic:** ______________________

Correct the punctuation.

8 In the 1960's Dads favourite programme was Doctor Who.

9 The club has lost two of it's best players.

10 Do'nt knock on stranger's doors.



X There is only one correct answer. X There is more than one correct answer.

# Section 2 Test 12

## A WARM-UP

You are describing a deserted beach. Write under each heading two phrases that you could use.

**1** **sounds:** ______________________

______________________

**2** **textures:** ______________________

______________________

**3** **sights:** ______________________

______________________

Write the adverb that means

**4** with fury: ____________

**5** with suspicion: ____________

**6** with anxiety: ____________

**7** with mystery: ____________

**8** with malice: ____________

Complete the words by adding different affixes and/or root words.

**9** _____graph graph_____ _____graph_____

**10** _____verb verb_____ _____verb_____

## B WORD WORK

Write the words correctly.

**1** cathederal dergree specterum

______________________

**2** apperatus carberhydrate develerpment

______________________

**3** Are the words spelt correctly? Put a tick or cross.

discuss ___ disappoint ___

disolve ___ discide ___

**4** Write correctly the words that are wrongly spelt.

______________________

**5** Add the suffix that will make the words into verbs.

mod___ simpl___ qual___

**6** Add the suffix that will change the verbs into nouns.

______________________

Write the full version of the word.

**7** **lab** ____________

**8** **demo** ____________

**9** **exam** ____________

**10** **app** ____________

## C SENTENCE WORK

**1** Punctuate this sentence.

Oh really he replied sneering at the figure trembling before him.

**2** What is the purpose of the last part of the sentence?

______________________

Continue the sentence, combining dialogue and action.

**3** "I've some bad news ______________________

**4** "Stop right there ______________________

Continue the sentence as if you were writing to persuade.

**5** Obviously ______________________

**6** Regrettably ______________________

**7** Admittedly ______________________

Continue the sentence as if you were writing a newspaper report.

**8** Tragically ______________________

**9** Luckily ______________________

**10** What is the purpose of these adverbs?

______________________

**Now complete Section 2 of the Progress chart on page 46.**

# Section 2 Writing task: The nervous cyclist

## Task

'The nervous cyclist' is a story aimed at pupils aged 10 or 11 years. Write an opening for the story that will quickly engage the reader.

## Hints

Before you start:

- Decide on the story genre and what the story might be about.
- Who is the nervous cyclist? Where is the story set?
- Is the story **told by** the nervous cyclist or is the story **about** him or her?
- Think of an effective story opening.

As you write:

- Capture your reader's interest from the start.
- Think carefully as you choose your words and story-telling techniques.

*Continue on a separate sheet.*

## Check

- When you have finished, check through your story.
- Edit and proofread it.
- Make sure that everything looks and sounds right.

# Section 2 Proofreading task: Why we must go green

## Task

Proofread this text written for the **Go Green!** website.

### Hints

- Check that everything is clear and sounds right.
- Check that punctuation has been added correctly.
- Check the spelling of the words chosen.

Did you know avrage globel tempratures have increesed by all-most one dergree over the past sentury it doesnt sound like much does it but if this trend continnews it could change Earths climite compltely threatning our plannet and its frajile eko-systems.

A warmer Earth could permenantly effect many aspects of our plannet: rainfal patturns sea levels the ranje of plants and wildlife even the food we eat and the warter we drink.

When sceintists talk about climite change there consern is about globul warming corsed by human activitys, yes thats right the sauce of the problem is peopel.

You see burning fuals with carbbon in them thats oil, gas and coal adds to the natureal greenhouse layer in the lower atmossfere trapping more heat and so causeing the earth to warm up.

Cars airoplanes power statons and factoryes they all contrabute to globeal warming so actuly we are all responsable.

### Extra

Now write the wording for a poster that explains one way in which humans contribute to the environmental problems facing the Earth and one way in which we could do something positive to help. Use a separate sheet of paper for your writing.

# Section 3 Test 1

## A WARM-UP

Expand the nouns to add more detail to this list of items on a menu.

1 ______________________ guinea fowl
______________________

2 ______________________ salad
______________________

3 ______________________ lamb
______________________

4 ______________________ salmon
______________________

5 Make three words using these letters and graphemes only. **t b augh ough**

______________________

6 Add the same grapheme to all the words.

___orus ___oir ___ord or___estra

Complete the word sum.

7 _____ + **access** + _____ = __________

8 _____ + **nation** + _____ = __________

9 **edit** + _____ + _____ = __________

10 **civil** + _____ + _____ = __________

## B WORD WORK

Add the missing syllables to complete the

1 **abstract nouns:**

gen / _____ / _____ / i / ty **Clue:** *kindness*

mis / _____ / _____ **Clue:** *bad luck*

2 **adverbs:**

def / _____ / _____ / ly **Clue:** *without doubt*

ab / _____ / _____ / _____ **Clue:** *completely*

3 **adjectives:**

mem / _____ / _____ / ble **Clue:** *unforgettable*

in / _____ / _____ **Clue:** *not guilty*

Write two words derived from the root.

4 **depend** ______________________

5 **value** ______________________

6 **moral** ______________________

7 **serve** ______________________

Write sentences to show three different meanings of the word **force**.

8 ______________________

9 ______________________

10 ______________________

## C SENTENCE WORK

Write four sentences using these words only.

**read the letter Miss Levy when she was alone smiling to herself**

1 ______________________

2 ______________________

3 ______________________

4 ______________________

5 Why is the second of these sentences more effective than the first?

**Smoking is harmful because it can kill you.** **Smoking is harmful: it can kill you.**

______________________

Add a colon and cross out any unnecessary words.

6 There is only one way forward and that is to cut emissions.

7 You can make a difference if you join the great recycle.

You are writing a discussion text. Give three connecting phrases that would help you to

8 **illustrate a point:** ______________________

9 **add another point:** ______________________

10 **oppose or balance:** ______________________



X There is only one correct answer. X There is more than one correct answer.

# Section 3 Test 2

## A WARM-UP

Add a relative clause giving extra information.

1 Try our new range, ______________________

______________________

2 Our products are tested by specialists ______

______________________

3 This is a product ______________________

______________________

Add the missing letters.

4 r_r_l  v_w_l  m_j_r  d_g_t

5 _nd_x  _x_t  _tl_s  _rb_n

6 Underline the words that are wrongly spelt.

modurn  patturn  trodden  flatten

7 Write the correct spelling.

______________________

Complete the compound word chain.

8 fire**wood** – **wood**wind – __________

9 shorthand – __________ – __________

10 underpass – __________ – __________

## B WORD WORK

1 Write the words as plurals.

**prefix** __________  **cactus** __________

**axis** __________  **gazebo** __________

**video** __________  **gateau** __________

Add the same prefix to all three words.

2 _____bacterial  _____-racist  _____body

3 _____hand  _____ground  _____cast

4 _____ordinate  _____standard  _____merge

Write three more words with each prefix.

5 ______________________

6 ______________________

7 ______________________

Write two synonyms of the word(s) in **bold**.

8 It was **mainly** dry. __________

9 It seemed **a little** odd. __________

10 He is **fully** recovered. __________

## C SENTENCE WORK

The flickering candlelight picked out a long table with heavily carved chairs an empty fireplace dusty drapes at darkened windows portraits of unwelcoming faces and in the corner amongst the shadows stood a grotesque statue-like figure.

1 Punctuate the sentence.

2 Underline four noun phrases that create a sense of unease.

3 How does the sentence structure contribute to the dramatic effect? ______________________

______________________

Continue the sentence, creating a contrast to follow the semi-colon.

4 Latika was successful; ______________________

5 Mark was always there on time; ______________________

6 I enjoyed the film; ______________________

7 Reginald Jenkins was born in poverty; ______________________

Add the correct word. **less fewer**

8 I am trying to eat __________ sugar and drink __________ sugary drinks.

9 There were __________ visitors this year so we raised __________ money than expected.

10 Many people find they have __________ time available and attend __________ classes.

X There is only one correct answer.  X There is more than one correct answer.

# Section 3 Test 3

## A WARM-UP

Modify the sentence to create a clear mood.

1 Clouds drift. ______________________

______________________

2 Children scream. ______________________

______________________

3 Lights twinkle. ______________________

______________________

What could the word be? Write three possibilities.

4 p_st_l ______________________

5 m_n_s ______________________

6 d_c_d_ ______________________

Write three synonyms.

7 **anxiously**

______________________

8 **bravely**

______________________

9 **warily**

______________________

10 **nimbly**

______________________

## B WORD WORK

1 Add the missing letters.

**c s cc ss sc**

a___e___ ne___e___ary su___e___

pro___e___ ___in___erely di___ern

___in___ere adole___en___e de___i___ion

Add the missing syllable or syllables.

2 ac / _____ / dent *Clue: a mishap*

3 dis / _____ / line *Clue: regulation, control*

4 de / _____ / tion *Clue: dishonesty*

5 fas / _____ / nate *Clue: to intrigue*

6 Write one word that is related to each word above.

______________________

______________________

Write a sentence using the word as a verb.

7 **snake:** ______________________

8 **panic:** ______________________

9 **pilot:** ______________________

10 **slave:** ______________________

## C SENTENCE WORK

Add to the start of the sentence a clause that gives a reason.

1 ______________________ we are planning to hire a juggler.

2 ______________________ we hope to improve the centre.

3 ______________________ the work has not yet been completed.

Add the missing punctuation.

4 Di blinked Not now she whispered shaking her head I need time to think

5 You Joel said pointing to Nigel You will pay for this

6 Ive bin speakin to t master Edgar began

7 You aint comin in said Mrs Noon barring the door

Write the opening sentence for a mystery story.

8 **dialogue:** ______________________

9 **short sentence:** ______________________

10 **complex sentence:** ______________________

______________________



X There is only one correct answer. X There is more than one correct answer.

# Section 3 Test 4

## A WARM-UP

Continue the advertisement choosing suitable words.

1 Experience the West Indies: ____________

____________

2 Safeguard your skin: ____________

____________

3 Chocolate for grown-ups: ____________

____________

Write six words with this ending.

4 **idge** ____________

____________

5 **age** ____________

____________

6 **ture** ____________

____________

Add the missing letters.

7 l _ r _ c

8 v _ r _ s

9 m _ th _ d

10 m _ d _ m

## B WORD WORK

Cross out the words that are wrongly spelt. Write the correct spelling.

1 The sucses of the sceme depends on this facter. ____________

2 This isshue shuold remain seperate.

____________

3 In genral, results of the trile were encurageing. ____________

Write a word that begins with the root.

4 **mono** ____________ 5 **corp(us)** ____________

Write the meaning of the root.

6 **mono:** ____________ 7 **corp(us):** ____________

Write a definition of the word in **bold**.

8 Their movements were **synchronised**.

synchronised: ____________

____________

9 It was just about **tolerable**.

tolerable: ____________

10 The artist character is a **stereotype**.

stereotype: ____________

____________

## C SENTENCE WORK

**Police catch man with butterfly net**
**Stolen car abandoned by river**
**School dinners protest**
**Medics help snake bite victim**

1 Why are the newspaper headlines confusing? ____________

Write each headline as a clear and complete sentence – as if it were in the main part of the article.

2 ____________

3 ____________

4 ____________

5 ____________

Add brackets within the sentence.

6 I wouldn't help him for a million pounds although the money would be rather tempting.

7 Katie volunteered what a surprise to help.

8 I said the car was definitely blue that's correct, isn't it? and old.

9 What do the brackets contribute to the tone of the sentence?

____________

10 Continue the sentence using imagery and alliteration.

Outside ____________

X There is only one correct answer. X There is more than one correct answer.

# Section 3 Test 5

## A WARM-UP

Write three sentences using the word **carrot**, to appear in

**1** **a newspaper:** ______________________

______________________

**2** **instructions:** ______________________

______________________

**3** **a story:** ______________________

______________________

**4** Underline the words that are spelt correctly.

**design desease deny dessolve devide**

**5** Write correctly the words that are wrongly spelt.

______________________

Add a second syllable.

**6** hic / ____ **7** tis / ____

Add the same root word to all three words.

**8** re____ ____ionnaire ____ion

**9** un____n ____ledge ____ing

**10** ____folio pass____ ____er

## B WORD WORK

Add the correct ending.

**1** **ance ence**

bal____ prefer____ relev____

**2** **ent ant**

relev____ independ____ adjac____

**3** **ar er or**

gramm____ offend____ trait____

Write three words beginning with

**4** **uni:** ______________________

**5** **multi:** ______________________

Write different definitions of each word.

**6** **cell** (in IT): ______________________

**7** **cell** (in biology): ______________________

______________________

**8** **cell** (in everyday use): ______________________

**9** **monitor** (in IT): ______________________

**10** **monitor** (verb): ______________________

## C SENTENCE WORK

**1** Punctuate the sentence with commas and a semi-colon.

Springing to her feet Angela's expression clouded anger flickering in her eyes she grabbed her coat let out a tirade of abuse and stormed out of the door

**2** What is the effect of this sentence construction? ______________________

**3** Compose a similar sentence describing a desperate search.

______________________

______________________

Briefly explain how the idea is different in each of the sentences.

**4** **I must go to the gym later.** ______________________

**5** **I might go to the gym later.** ______________________

**6** **I will go to the gym later.** ______________________

**7** **I should go to the gym later.** ______________________

**8** **I can go the gym later.** ______________________

**9** Underline the words above that make the difference between sentences.

**10** Rewrite the sentence as a possibility rather than a statement of fact.

**Johal was there.** ______________________



X There is only one correct answer. X There is more than one correct answer.

# Section 3 Test 6

## A WARM-UP

Complete the complex sentence.

1 I stood on the edge ______________________

______________________

2 ______________________

______________ I stood on the edge

______________________

Complete the word sum.
Start the sum with an antonym prefix.

3 ______ + move + ______ = ______________

4 ______ + resist + ______ = ______________

5 ______ + flame + ______ = ______________

Write the adverb that means

6 with energy: ______________

7 with imagination: ______________

8 with compassion: ______________

9 with regret: ______________

10 with menace: ______________

## B WORD WORK

Cross out the words that are wrongly spelt in the headline. Write the correct spelling.

1 Portrate exibition opens at gallary

______________________

2 Applorse for amature theater group

______________________

3 Govament desision 'riddiculus'

______________________

Write two words that begin with the root

4 **bene** (meaning **well**):

______________________

5 **bio(s)** (meaning **life**):

______________________

Write sentences to show the different meanings of these near synonyms for **change**.

6 **alter:** ______________________

7 **correct:** ______________________

8 **vary:** ______________________

9 **reorganise:** ______________________

10 **transform:** ______________________

## C SENTENCE WORK

1 **The butler lay dead on the floor.**

**The butler lay, dead, on the floor.**

Why has the writer added the commas? ______________________

Add commas that perform a similar function.

2 I lay there terrified waiting for the noise to stop.

3 They walked fearfully into the room.

Write an example of your own. 4 ______________________

Why is the headline amusing?

5 Giant police hunt for jewel thief ______________________

6 Students make a tasty meal ______________________

7 Robson's back under pressure ______________________

Explain two possible purposes of

8 **a leaflet for Town Farm:** ______________________

9 **an eyewitness account of a tornado:** ______________________

10 **a newspaper report about a protest march:** ______________________

X There is only one correct answer. X There is more than one correct answer.

# Section 3 Test 7

## A WARM-UP

Continue the sentence.

1 So, I'd failed – ____________________

2 Nobody noticed – ____________________

Add the missing syllables.

3 un / ______ / ______ / ______ / ly
*Clue: unluckily*

4 con / ______ / ______ / ______
*Clue: as a result*

5 ap / ______ / ______ / ______ / ______
*Clue: about, roughly*

6 Make six words using all or some of these letters and no others. You may use a letter more than once if necessary.

**c s u a e i** ____________________

____________________

Add a two- or three-letter word to complete the longer word.

7 em____rass

8 ca____dral

9 sy____nym

10 be____ve

## B WORD WORK

1 Write in the tricky part of each word.

sil______ette b______tiful man______vre

2 Write the correct spelling.

miniture ____________ aquired ____________

3 Underline the correct spelling.

forfill forfil fulfill fullfil fulfil

Add the suffix that changes the words into

4 **verbs:** public____ memory____

5 **abstract nouns:** cruel____ scarce____

6 **nouns naming places:** bake____ pot____

Write a sentence to show the meaning of

7 **conscience:** ____________________

8 **conscious:** ____________________

9 **practise** (verb): ____________________

10 **practice** (noun): ____________________

## C SENTENCE WORK

**The man fled he was leaving his home leaving his possessions leaving his past behind.**

1 Punctuate the sentence using a colon and commas.

Give two techniques that the writer has used to make the sentence effective.

2 ____________________

3 ____________________

Underline the two verbs that you find the most emotive.

4 kill slaughter execute exterminate

5 cut slash reduce axe

6 chase hound follow stalk

7 Explain why these verbs are emotive.

____________________

**Some people want to paint the room red.**

Counter this idea with a sentence that

8 **is dismissive:** ____________________

9 **uses evidence to refute it:** ____________________

10 **shows it is a weak idea:** ____________________



X There is only one correct answer. X There is more than one correct answer.

# Section 3 Test 8

## A WARM-UP

Write a dramatic sentence containing no more than five words.

1 ______
2 ______
3 ______
4 ______
______

Write the word beside its definition.

**bilingual cinquain triad unilateral**

5 ______ chord of three notes
6 ______ able to speak two languages
7 ______ one sided
8 ______ poem of five lines

Form ten words using these word parts. Add each word to the correct category.

**tour organ vandal bapt ist ism ise**

9 **nouns:** ______
______
10 **verbs:** ______

## B WORD WORK

Write the correct spelling.

1 circumfrance ______
isoscelles ______
2 gess ______
approxamate ______
3 avrage ______
devision ______

Write three words derived from the root.

4 **believe** ______
5 **force** ______
6 **examine** ______

Write different definitions of each word.

7 **consumer** (in D&T): ______
______
8 **consumer** (in science): ______
______
9 **producer** (in drama): ______
______
10 **producer** (in science): ______
______

## C SENTENCE WORK

Rewrite the sentence using a colon for effect.

1 The only hope they had left was the raft. ______
2 Climate change is a new threat to the survival of animals. ______
______
3 Our victory was the result of determination and teamwork. ______
______

What do the following tell you about what is to come?

4 However, despite some successes … ______
5 The main difference between … ______
6 Since then … ______
7 All of these ideas … ______

Rework the transcript into formal Standard English.

8 We was goin' up town but the fog wus bad. ______
9 Her knew a'right, but her din say nothing. ______
10 Me and Jim we both 'ad one of them games what was on the telly. ______
______

X There is only one correct answer. X There is more than one correct answer.

# Section 3 Test 9

## A WARM-UP

Complete the sentence.

1 Pausing ______________________

______________________

2 Frowning ______________________

______________________

3 Fighting ______________________

______________________

Add the correct word.

**less fewer**

4 Today, ______ people walk to work.

5 Mrs Jones now has ______ money.

6 I worked ______ hours; I earned ______ pay.

7 ______ cows means ______ milk.

Make the words into

8 **adjectives:**

space______ allergy______ race______

9 **nouns:**

accurate______ generous______ aware______

10 **nouns:**

assist______ rehearse______ attach______

## B WORD WORK

Write three words related to the word in **bold**.

1 **prefer**

______________________

2 **define**

______________________

3 **sign**

______________________

4 **person**

______________________

Write two words ending in

5 **logue:** ______________________

6 **logy:** ______________________

7 **graphy:** ______________________

Underline the root and write a definition.

8 **deforestation:** ______________________

______________________

9 **unsystematic:** ______________________

10 **aromatic:** ______________________

## C SENTENCE WORK

**Hi, Em. You off swimming? Yeah ... no worries. See you tomorrow. About 10.**

What clues tell you that this is spoken language?

1 **word clues:** ______________________

2 **sentence clues:** ______________________

3 **content clues:** ______________________

**I saw Emma earlier. She was carrying her kit bag, which meant she was going swimming. She said she was in a rush so I said I'd meet her tomorrow at 10 a.m.**

What clues tell you that this is written text?

4 **word clues:** ______________________

5 **sentence clues:** ______________________

6 **content clues:** ______________________

Continue the sentence, combining speech and actions.

7 Turning to ______________________

8 "She's ______________________

9 Aaron ______________________

10 "Sir ______________________



X There is only one correct answer. X There is more than one correct answer.

# Section 3 Test 10

## A WARM-UP

Add a subordinate clause.

1 Ricky agreed at once ______________________

______________________

2 Ricky ______________________ agreed at once.

3 ______________________ Ricky agreed at once.

Make two words by adding different prefixes and suffixes.

4 _____press_____ _____press_____

5 _____port_____ _____port_____

6 Make the words into verbs.

advert_____ solid_____ origin_____

Add the missing syllables.

7 ma / _____ / _____ / _____ *Clue: fabric*

8 dis / _____ / _____ / _____ *Clue: a drawback*

9 con / _____ / _____ *Clue: not a vowel*

10 ho / _____ / _____ / _____ *Clue: not vertical*

## B WORD WORK

1 Write the root word.

**vegetation** __________

**liquefy** __________

**specification** __________

Write a definition.

2 **vegetation:** ______________________

3 **liquefy:** ______________________

4 **specification:** ______________________

______________________

One consonant or two? Add the missing letters.

5 o___a___iona___y **(c s l)**

6 di___a___ea___ance **(s p r)**

7 pa___a___e___ **(r l l)**

8 a___a___a___us **(p r t)**

Write three synonyms of the word in **bold**.

9 It was **very** cold.

______________________

10 You could hear it **sometimes**.

______________________

## C SENTENCE WORK

**That night, they came. That night, they crept closer. That night, they slipped unseen through countless windows.**

What techniques has the writer used to build tension?

1 ______________________ 2 ______________________

Write a similar set of sentences.

3 Slowly ______________________

______________________

4 Now ______________________

Underline the adverbs and explain their effect on the meaning.

5 Many children now skip breakfast. ______________________

6 Yet we have still had no reply. ______________________

7 Mrs Bassi was again disturbed. ______________________

Add a colon and continue the sentence.

8 Everything was in place ______________________

9 Ajit remembered how it had felt to fly ______________________

10 The situation was grim ______________________

X There is only one correct answer. X There is more than one correct answer.

# Section 3 Test 11

## A WARM-UP

Write three sentences using the word **mysterious**.

1 **newspaper report:** ____________________

____________________

2 **advert:** ____________________

____________________

3 **description:** ____________________

____________________

Complete the word sum.

4 **graph** + ____ + ____ + ____ = ____________
5 **strategy** + ____ + ____ + ____ = ____________
6 ____ + **fortune** + ____ + ____ = ____________
7 ____ + **emote** + ____ + ____ = ____________

Write the word beside its definition.

**resplendent multifarious verbose**

8 ____________ with great variety
9 ____________ wordy; long-winded
10 ____________ dazzling, gloriously bright

## B WORD WORK

Add the missing vowels.

1 cap_ble ed_ble sol_ble
2 audi_nce coher_nce bal_nce
3 haz_rd meth_d gramm_r jarg_n

Write a verb, an adjective and a noun based on the root – and label each one.

4 **econ** ____________________

____________________

5 **class** ____________________

____________________

6 **medic** ____________________

____________________

Write different definitions.

7 **solution** (in science):

____________________

8 **solution** (in PSHE): ____________________

____________________

9 **tension** (in drama and PHSE): ____________________

____________________

10 **tension** (in D&T and science): ____________________

## C SENTENCE WORK

1 Punctuate this sentence so that it reads effectively.

**She dreamt about a room an empty room an empty room with no windows a room with no way in and no way out.**

2 What makes the sentence structure effective?

____________________

3 How does the punctuation help? ____________________

4 What other technique has the writer used? ____________

Continue the dialogue using Standard English.

5 "Well," ____________________

6 Rose ____________________

Continue the dialogue using non-Standard English.

7 "Well," ____________________

8 Rose ____________________

____________________

Add a proper noun and a possessive pronoun to complete the text.

9 Len and Joe found the instructions. ________ began to read, following the text with ________ finger.

10 Meanwhile, ________ eyes flitted from piece to piece, assembling the model in ________ mind.



X There is only one correct answer. X There is more than one correct answer.

# Section 3 Test 12

## A WARM-UP

Write an acronym sentence based on the word in **bold**. Then circle the letters that form the acronym.

1 **time:** ____________________

____________________

2 **smile:** ____________________

____________________

3 **towns:** ____________________

____________________

Complete the word table.

| | verb | adjective | noun |
|---|---|---|---|
| 4 | **exhaust** | | |
| 5 | **collect** | | |
| 6 | **agree** | | |
| 7 | **impress** | | |

What does the instrument record?

8 **thermograph** ____________

9 **seismograph** ____________

10 **chronograph** ____________

## B WORD WORK

Add the correct word.

**effect affect**

1 Weather conditions may ________ the results.

2 The change will have an ________ on us all.

3 I can't let this ________ my performance.

4 Measles can ________ the nervous system.

Add the missing vowels.

5 ***Clue:*** *nourishing*

n___tr___t___s

6 ***Clue:*** *polite; relating to society*

c___v___l

7 Write two nouns related to each adjective above.

____________________

Write a scientific definition.

8 **germ:** ____________________

____________________

9 **vertebrate:** ____________________

10 **microclimate:** ____________________

## C SENTENCE WORK

**They called the man Jack yes, that was right but what was the other man's name he was sure it was a name he knew it was floating tantalisingly in his mind just out of reach wait a moment come on yes William that was it**

1 Add punctuation and capital letters to make the passage read effectively.

2 What effect is created by the sentence structure? ____________________

3 Continue the text with another sentence. ____________________

Strengthen the argument by adding a phrase or clause after the noun.

4 Parents ____________________ demand answers.

5 All people ____________________ should protest.

6 Anyone ____________________ will be appalled at this decision.

7 Local residents ____________________ are writing to the council.

Write the first two lines of a

8 **ballad:** ____________________

____________________

9 **haiku:** ____________________

____________________

10 **limerick:** ____________________

____________________

Now complete Section 3 of the Progress chart on page 46.

# Section 3 Writing task: Launchpad local

## Task

Your local council wants to promote the facilities and activities provided for young people in your area through its 'Launchpad local' scheme. Your task is to write a leaflet aimed at these young people, which gives this information in a positive and appealing way.

## Hints

Before you start:

- Decide what information to include.
- Consider the needs and interests of your readers. Are these catered for at present, and if so how?
- How will you organise your information effectively?
- How will you present this information in an appealing and persuasive way?

As you write:

- Think about your purpose and audience.
- Choose carefully both your words and your way of expressing the ideas.

*Continue on a separate sheet.*

## Check

- When you have finished, check through your writing.
- Edit and proofread it.
- Make sure that everything looks and sounds right.

# Section 3 Proofreading task: Megan's mystery

## Task

Proofread this story extract.

## Hints

- Check that everything is expressed clearly and sounds right.
- Check that the punctuation has been used correctly and effectively.
- Check the spelling.

The coridoor was diserted the classrooms was diserted their was no movments no voises no sounds of eny sort it was as if the school had been mommenterilly frozern in time.

Megan had just one thorght to find the diary she had spent all day perswading herself that this was defernatly the only way. Obviusly if Mr Neil caght her she would have to take the concequences that was the risk a risk she was prapared to take it was her only chanse was'nt it it was a neccesery risk.

Cautiusly she stole down the corridor nerveusly checking the libruary before reaching Mr Neils room she entered buisnesslike she headed straght for Mr Neils desk searching with concenttration folowing her carefulyplaned stratigy leaveing no evidense.

Then suddenlly what was that. Footsteps voises ... a voise she recergnised right outside the door she froze terryfied waiting to be disscoverd.

## Extra

The last thing that happens (see above) is that Megan hears a voice. On a separate sheet of paper, write down the words that she hears. Then continue the story.

# English Skills 6 Progress chart

| Name | Class/Set |
|---|---|
| Teacher's name | Date |

## Instructions

Read the **'I can' targets** for the section you have just finished.

- Colour the circle **green** if you find it **easy** to do what is described.
- Colour the circle **orange** if you are **getting there**, but still need to work on it.
- Colour the circle **red** if you still find this a **difficult** thing to do.

If there are things that you still find difficult you can work on them in the next section or ask your teacher for help.

## Writing sentences

| 'I can' targets | Section 1 | Section 2 | Section 3 |
|---|---|---|---|
| I can vary sentence length and type to achieve different effects. | ○ | ○ | ○ |
| I can form complex sentences using different types of subordinate clause. | ○ | ○ | ○ |
| I can use conditional sentences to show that one event depends upon another. | ○ | ○ | ○ |
| I can use passives to alter the focus and/or the formality of a sentence. | ○ | ○ | ○ |
| I can vary the order of phrases and clauses for emphasis and effect. | ○ | ○ | ○ |
| I can use appropriate sentence structures for different genres and purposes. | | | ○ |
| I can create noun phrases using adjectives, prepositions and relative clauses. | | | |

## Using punctuation

| 'I can' targets | Section 1 | Section 2 | Section 3 |
|---|---|---|---|
| I can use punctuation to mark the boundaries between sentences and clauses. | ○ | ○ | ○ |
| I can use apostrophes for possession and in shortened forms. | ○ | ○ | ○ |
| I can write sentences using colons, dashes, brackets and semi-colons. | ○ | ○ | ○ |
| I can put direct speech into longer sentences and punctuate them correctly. | | ○ | ○ |
| I can use punctuation to convey or clarify meaning. | | | ○ |
| I can use punctuation to create effects (e.g., to vary pace). | | | ○ |

## Checking grammar

| 'I can' targets | Section 1 | Section 2 | Section 3 |
|---|---|---|---|
| I can use different verb tenses or forms, including modals, to fit the purpose. | ○ | ○ | ○ |
| I can use the grammar and stylistic features of different text types. | ○ | ○ | ○ |
| I can use pronouns correctly, avoiding repetition and ambiguity. | | ○ | ○ |
| I can use Standard English in formal writing when appropriate. | | ○ | ○ |
| I can recognise ambiguity and know when to avoid or use it. | | ○ | ○ |

## Understanding and choosing words

| 'I can' targets | Section 1 | Section 2 | Section 3 |
|---|---|---|---|
| I can use context, word structure and origin to work out word meanings. | ○ | ○ | ○ |
| I can distinguish between different uses of a word (e.g., as a noun or as a verb). | ○ | ○ | ○ |
| I can use both imagery (e.g., similes) and sound effects (e.g., rhyme). | ○ | ○ | ○ |
| I can choose precise vocabulary for effect or to make inferences. | ○ | ○ | ○ |
| I can use appropriate connectives as signposts within a text. | | | ○ |

## Spelling

| 'I can' targets | Section 1 | Section 2 | Section 3 |
|---|---|---|---|
| I can spell longer words using syllables and word structure (e.g., affixes). | ○ | ○ | ○ |
| I can use spelling rules and know common exceptions. | ○ | ○ | ○ |
| I can choose the correct spelling of homophones/commonly-confused words. | ○ | ○ | ○ |
| I can use strategies that help me to spell words with unstressed vowels. | ○ | ○ | ○ |
| I can choose the correct spelling of similar endings (e.g., **ary/ory/ery**). | ○ | ○ | ○ |
| I can spell tricky words (e.g., **rhyme**, **issue**, **success**, **necessary**, **parallel**). | ○ | ○ | ○ |
| I can use analogy and letter strings to help with spelling (e.g., **ough**, **aught**). | ○ | ○ | ○ |